The Shift Stirrer Method

—

A FIVE STEP
MINDFULNESS METHOD
TO GET YOUR SH*T
TOGETHER & SHIFT YOUR
PERCEPTION

TINAMARIE CLARK

TO MY MOM
MY GREATEST TEACHER

—

Thank you for always encouraging
me to look inward…we did it.

CONTENTS

To You, My Brave, and Courageous Shift Stirrer!

I am so excited for you to take this journey of self-discovery! This workbook is not for the faint of heart but you my dear are not that. You are brave and I bow to your willingness to look at your sh*t.

Always,

Tina Marie Clark

THE FIVE STEPS

—

STIR: Becoming aware you have shifted into a negative thought pattern.

—

SIT in communion with negative thoughts and emotions without reacting.

—

SIFT through all of the thoughts, beliefs, and emotions related to your stir story.

—

SHARE your vulnerable stir story and what came up in the <u>sit</u> and the <u>sift</u>.

—

SHIFT your perception through the wisdom that has been unearthed from working the steps.

MY STORY

—

"Life is about growth, renewal, and transformation. We are all capable of immense positive change. The beauty is in the shift."
TINAMARIE CLARK

My path as a Shift Stirrer begins with my humble roots as a kid growing up in the suburbs of Philadelphia. I was raised in government-assisted Section 8 housing by my fiercely loving single mother, two older brothers Matt and Wayne, and younger sister Brianna. Our messy home, second hand clothes, and old beater car always stuck out. To this day, the smell of mildew on laundry can instantly bring me back to those days. My brothers and I were known as the bad, poor kids. I felt branded by our circumstances and struggled with a persistent sense of shame.

In reality, I was a sweet, thoughtful, and focused child who daydreamed about having a modeling career in New York City, Paris, and Milan. But to the outside world I presented someone completely different. My family's code of honor and deepest-held tribal belief said that to be feared was safer than being seen. I was defensive, combative, and rough around the edges. I armored up with verbal knives, emotional swords, and a me-against-the-world mentality that masked my deep shame. I threatened peers, told off teachers, threw chairs in fits of rage. Between sixth and twelfth grade I was expelled from six different schools. By the grace of God, I was finally placed at Lakeside Educational Network where teachers were well equipped to deal with someone like me. They saw through my rage and understood my pain. I am eternally grateful for the education and relationships I developed at Lakeside.

At 15 years old my dream came true and I landed my first modeling contract. But at my first booking I battled it out with a fellow model over a pair of shoes and nearly derailed my career. The next morning I received a sobering wake-up call and stern warning from my agent, which made me realize that if I wanted a shot at my dream I had to choose another way to be.

It was time to lay down my sword.

Modeling was the catalyst for the dramatic internal shift I so desperately needed. As I slipped into beautiful designer gowns every day, I could not wear my old emotional armor if I wanted to succeed. I would have to shed my defensive layers and embrace a softer, kinder persona.

So I committed to unwinding my old beliefs. I devoured self-help books, threw myself into intensive workshops, sat with my thoughts, and had raw conversations with close girlfriends and family. I spent hours on the phone with my mom, who consistently said, "I know you think this is about (fill in the blank), but I promise, it's about you." She prompted me to look inside myself and take responsibility for the part I played in my own suffering. To do so meant facing my own fears, worries, and flaws—no matter how ugly.

As I began uncovering more of my true self, my bonds with my friends became more authentic and my connection with my partner deepened. That first modeling contract eventually led to an incredible career.

The little girl afraid of showing weakness is still a part of me and is sometimes afraid. But now she's grown into a woman who feels an exhilarating strength and desire to share her full and imperfect self.

A shift stirred inside me, and I've fallen in love with the real Tinamarie. I want that shift for you, too.

When we open ourselves up, we can receive gifts beyond our wildest imaginations. My dream is that we all dare to STIR, SIT, SIFT, SHARE, and SHIFT. In this workbook I show you how to work the steps and #ownyourawful.

Always,

Tina Marie Clark

STEP *1*

STIR: Becoming aware
you have shifted into a
negative thought pattern.

*"You know that discomfort
you're feeling? Yeah. That is
your internal guide telling
you to SIT, SIFT, and
SHARE so you can SHIFT."*

TINAMARIE CLARK

Step 1: STIR

—

When you are active in a STIR, it is as if you've been instantly transported into an emotional tornado engulfed by thoughts, beliefs, and emotions produced by FEAR.

You cannot see anything outside the walls of this storm, no matter how beautiful the world may be. Most of the dialogue occurring within the mind is happening without your conscious awareness and is often perceived as fact. When consumed with these debilitating thoughts, it causes immense emotional pain and suffering. This discomfort is your signal that you're active in a stir story. I call this experience being in the "I" of the stir, which is the part of you that is identifying with the ego's false narrative.

Think of your stir stories as individual books in your internal library. All of the stir stories are active and have never been fully processed. Some of these stories have been dormant for years and have never seen the light of day! Some you may be too ashamed to look at and others are too long to read. There are some you've inherited, some that date as far back as your infancy and others as new as yesterday.

All these stir stories wreak havoc on your body and mind. They rear their heads at the most inopportune times.

It is your responsibility to take one of these stir stories off the shelf, crack it open, and run it through the Shift Stirrer Method trusting you will find peace on the other side.

Liberate yourself from the shackles of your stir stories.

This method requires courage, honesty, chutzpah, and a desire to be FREE. I promise you that if you work this method you can learn to get out of your own way. So buckle up as we peel the layers of your stir stories so you can live the life you have always wanted.

The Shift Stirrer Method

ANATOMY
OF THE STIR

—

Reactions

Default Defenses

Emotions

Beliefs

Thoughts

Stir

The Components
of a Stir

This exercise is designed to help cultivate awareness and identify your personal symptoms during a stir. Please review the list below and check all the physical and emotional symptoms that apply.

PHYSICAL SYMPTOMS

- ○ A stomach ache
- ○ Sweating
- ○ Hot sensations
- ○ Tingling
- ○ Panic attacks
- ○ Racing heart
- ○ Tense facial expressions
- ○ Nail biting
- ○ Inability to make eye contact
- ○ Loss of appetite
- ○ Shaking
- ○ Fainting
- ○ Fatigue
- ○ Pain
- ○ Muscle tension
- ○ Goosebumps
- ○ Pain
- ○ Numb
- ○ Racing heartbeat
- ○ Lightheadedness
- ○ Chills
- ○ Feeling paralyzed

EMOTIONAL SYMPTOMS

- ○ Anger
- ○ Depressed
- ○ Rage
- ○ Overwhelm
- ○ Defensiveness
- ○ Agitation
- ○ Withdrawnness
- ○ Panic
- ○ Fear
- ○ Sadness
- ○ Flashbacks
- ○ Anxiety
- ○ Excessive laughter
- ○ Feeling awkward
- ○ Catastrophic thinking
- ○ Confusion
- ○ Shame
- ○ Embarrassment
- ○ Shock
- ○ Denial
- ○ Disbelief
- ○ Difficulty concentrating

- ○ Irritability
- ○ Mood swings
- ○ Guilt
- ○ Self-blame
- ○ Hopelessness
- ○ Disconnectedness
- ○ Loneliness
- ○ Feeling of abandonment
- ○ Frustration
- ○ Feeling out of control
- ○ Vulnerability
- ○ Wanting to flee
- ○ Wanting to disappear
- ○ Wanting to Hide
- ○ Wanting to crawl out of my skin
- ○ Other _____
- ○ Other _____
- ○ Other _____
- ○ Other _____
- ○ Other _____

The Shift Stirrer Method

Pick a story that's currently upsetting you—something that's annoying you or causing you anxiety or pain. Set aside 10 minutes to write the unfiltered stir story. Describe the sequence of events and illuminate it in detail. This is your time and space to share the rawest version of it.

Step 1: STIR

_____

_____

_____

_____

_____

_____

_____

_____

_____

_____

_____

_____

The Shift Stirrer Method

Step 1: STIR

Name three feelings that describe your stir story.

1. _____

2. _____

3. _____

Pick a color that describes the stir.

_____

When you are in the "I" of the stir, your ego is grasping for evidence to convince and validate what you're feeling. It will generate the most nefarious thoughts or story lines to keep you stuck in suffering.

Now that You have dug into your STIR story. Let's SIT.

SIT in communion
with negative thoughts
and emotions without
reacting.

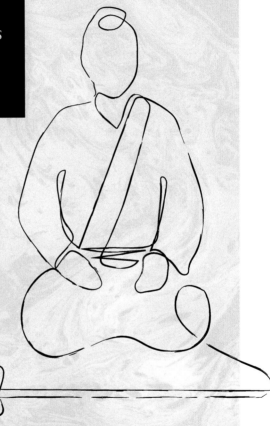

"On the other side of the SIT there are gifts."

TINAMARIE CLARK

SAMURAI AND THE SEIZA

For samurai warriors, an important component of their training was to sit in the seiza position. To sit seiza-style one must kneel on the floor and fold one's legs underneath one's thighs while resting the buttocks on the heels. This training in stillness was counterintuitive to the samurai warriors whose main training focused on hypervigilance and a readiness to attack or defend at any moment. For a samurai, the seiza was also a vulnerable position as it could hinder a warrior's ability to access his sword. But seiza training fortified a warrior's ability to control his reactions and understand his emotions. The expertise of the physical position requires discipline, self-mastery, and the ability to endure discomfort.

The embodiment of the seiza is not just about the physical state, but also the emotional state it bestows on its master. The samurai learned to sit within the discomfort of the position until it became less painful and more familiar. In mastery of the seiza, the samurai achieved strength, courage, and dominion over ego.

I consider The Shift Stirrer Method's SIT to be an emotional parallel to the Japanese seiza. Following a stir, the sit gives you a chance to feel any emotions you may be experiencing, look at them without taking action, and thus lessen their stronghold, just as the samurai did. The practice of the sit cultivates self-mastery, inner peace, and authentic power.

So surrender to the sit. At first it will feel uncomfortable, vulnerable, and counterintuitive. It will be extremely difficult to overcome your habit of reacting immediately. You will be tempted to come out of your sit in order to draw your usual emotional swords and shields. You will be tempted to revert to your normal default defenses, whatever they might be.

However, in practicing the sit you will gain stamina. As you begin, your goal is to build your endurance. Stay open. Your ego will fight you, and perhaps win the first, second or even third time, but the ego is your advisor not your king. The sit is a sacred space where the goal is listening to the ego, allowing it to speak to you, and honoring what it has to say without taking action.

With practice and self-discipline, your discomfort will decrease, your pain will soften, and the strength of your self-mastery will prevail. When you learn to surrender yourself to the sit, you will give yourself the ability to move through painful emotions and thoughts whilst maintaining stillness.

Just as the samurais struggled with the seiza, even the fiercest of warriors will find the sit challenging. However, with practice and nobility, self discipline can be attained.

Remember, the SIT is an active position, not a reactive nor passive one. This will most certainly feel uncomfortable at first, and may leave you feeling vulnerable.

The only way out is in.

THE SIT

Please always use the 24 hour rule:
While you're active in the stir and the sit, challenge yourself to avoid any outward reaction for at least 24 hours. This does not mean you should not stick up for yourself. There is a distinct difference between reacting and taking action. The sit creates space and time before you decide what action to take.

Start to consider what tactics you use to comfort and protect yourself during a stir. What are your typical Default Defenses?

Review the list below and check all that apply.

- ○ Act like everything's OK
- ○ Act super positive
- ○ Hide behind my spiritual practice or religion
- ○ Act like I don't care
- ○ People please
- ○ Make everyone agree with my version of the story
- ○ Attention seek
- ○ Starve or Binge eat
- ○ React on the inside not on the outside
- ○ Create walls around myself
- ○ Become passive aggressive
- ○ Insist on having the last word
- ○ Engage in OCD habits
- ○ Deny
- ○ Numb out
- ○ Drink too much alcohol
- ○ Mistreat people

- ○ Act violently
- ○ Oversleep or under sleep
- ○ Distract myself
- ○ Become a workaholic
- ○ Gossip or Critique others
- ○ Lie
- ○ Self-sabotage
- ○ Sabotage others
- ○ Gamble
- ○ Loose myself on social media
- ○ Blame others
- ○ Act overly dramatic
- ○ Over exercise
- ○ Watch Porn
- ○ Smoke
- ○ Inflict self-harm
- ○ Text my ex
- ○ Micro-manage
- ○ Getting into fights
- ○ Become needy
- ○ Create a crisis

- ○ Run away physically, mentally, spiritually, or emotionally
- ○ Become controlling
- ○ Rationalize
- ○ Fantasize
- ○ Disassociate
- ○ Act self-righteous
- ○ Minimize
- ○ Engage in codependent behaviors
- ○ Engage in risky behaviors
- ○ Become a perfectionist

- ○ Other _____
- ○ Other _____
- ○ Other _____
- ○ Other _____
- ○ Other _____

The Shift Stirrer Method

What is your most often used Default Defenses?

_____

_____

_____

Name three feelings that describe your SIT story.

1. _____

2. _____

3. _____

On a scale from 1-10 how difficult was your SIT? (Circle below)

1   2   3   4   5   6   7   8   9   10

Please use these powerful mantras to support you in the SIT.

"I will remain open no matter what."

"I am holding space for the unknown, so it can be revealed."

"Not today, Satan!"

"I will not say 'no' to this."

"The only way out is in."

"I know this is for me, I can SIT with this."

"What are you trying to show me?"

"Even if I can't see it now, there is something important here for me to see."

"Whatever you do, stay open."

"On the other side of the SIT, I know there is a gift for me."

"By remaining open in the SIT, my energy attracts that which I want."

"Show me the way."

"Ther e is something I am unable to see here."

"When I SIT, I change the energetic vibrations around me."

"In my softness I am my most powerful."

"The SIT is for me not them."

"I change my world when I SIT."

"All is well, even if it doesn't feel like it."

The Shift Stirrer Method

What SIT mantra resonated with you most?

STEP **3**

S I F T

SIFT through all of the thoughts, beliefs, and emotions related to your stir story.

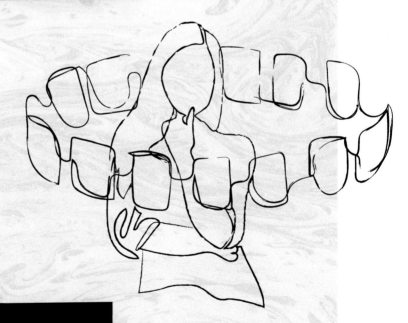

"The SIFT is where the source of your pain is revealed."

TINAMARIE CLARK

Step 3: SIFT

SHORT STORY

—

As a child, I would talk to my mother for hours, processing my stir stories as we spoke.

I would go on and on about how I had been wronged and layout all of my evidence. My mother would listen empathetically, but after most conversations would say the most infuriating and freeing sentence of all, "I know you think this is about (fill in the blank) but I promise you this is about you." It annoyed me to hear her say this, but my deeper knowing self was drawn to believe that what she was saying was true. If she was right, it would mean that I was creating my own drama on some level. The good news was that if I had the power to create the negative drama, I could also create something different. I had the ability to change what was going on inside of me with a simple yet counterintuitive shift of perception.

I remember asking, "Mom, how the hell could (fill in the blank) be about me?" She would then ask me about the thoughts I had had seconds after the incident. At first I found her questions difficult to answer because I was only aware of my reactions and at times my emotions. But the more I SIFTED, the better I was able to see my thoughts. This is when I discovered how lethal, debilitating, and manipulative my thoughts could be. It was as if I took a beating carried out by my mind itself.

The Shift Stirrer Method

Who wouldn't feel terrible after listening to such heinous things about themselves? I remember being shocked by how self-defeating and abusive my thoughts were about myself and others! I would often rely on my usual default defenses to protect myself by offloading my feelings on to others for momentary relief. The relief never lasted long. I knew there had to be another way.

The sift is where you #ownyourawful and get emphatically honest with yourself. This is where you make your subconscious conscious and begin to see the sources of your discomfort. It's where you look at the thoughts, beliefs, and narratives that are creating the stir. The sift is like an archaeological dig that uses nonjudgmental curiosity to uncover what is in the recesses of your mind.

This is why the sift is such an important step in Shift Stirrer Method. I believe that thoughts create emotions which create reactions. The sift is your chance to catch your thoughts red-handed and witness them robbing you of your joy and peace.

"To SHIFT it out you must SIFT it out."

TINAMARIE CLARK

Step 3: SIFT

This worksheet is designed to illuminate what you believe about yourself when you are active in a STIR.

Review the list below and check all STIR beliefs that apply.

○ Unloved	○ Flawed	○ Prey
○ Rejected	○ Exposed	○ Victimized
○ Disrespected	○ Disliked	○ Tricked
○ Broken	○ Too sensitive	○ Inappropriate
○ Discounted	○ Damaged goods	○ Deceived
○ Irrelevant	○ Rejected	○ Duped
○ Not a priority	○ A failure	○ Shamed
○ Less than	○ Impulsive	○ Tricked
○ Unworthy	○ A hot mess	○ Objectified
○ Dismissed	○ Out of control	○ Abused
○ Stupid	○ Undeserving	○ Used
○ Scared	○ Plagued	○ Dismissed
○ Sad	○ An outsider	○ Belittled
○ Weak	○ Betrayed	○ Hated
○ Desperate	○ The underdog	○ Not OK
○ Not enough	○ Imposed upon	○ Just who I am outcast
○ Unlucky	○ A disappointment	○ Traumatized
○ Unheard	○ A pushover	○ I always fuck this up
○ Ashamed	○ A pawn	○ I don't fit in
○ Embarrassed	○ Cheated	○ I wish things were different
○ Alone	○ A scape goat	
○ Lonely	○ A sacrifice	○ I don't have what it takes
○ Afraid	○ Innocent	
○ Hated		
○ Vulnerable		
○ Dumb		
○ Disconnected		

The Shift Stirrer Method

- ○ I always end up with a guy like this
- ○ I have the worst luck
- ○ Why me?
- ○ Why was I born into this family?
- ○ No one cares
- ○ Always going to feel this awful
- ○ No man will ever love me
- ○ I'll be alone forever
- ○ This always happens to me
- ○ Nobody listens to me
- ○ Life is against me
- ○ Always being one-upped
- ○ Look what you made me do
- ○ This is my parents' fault
- ○ Something is terribly wrong
- ○ No one wants to deal with what I've been through
- ○ Controlled
- ○ Manipulated

- ○ Not ready
- ○ A mess
- ○ Hopeless
- ○ Don't have time
- ○ Don't trust myself, I don't trust you
- ○ Too heavy
- ○ Too much
- ○ Too fat
- ○ Too poor
- ○ Too young
- ○ Too old
- ○ Too overweight

- ○ Other _____
- ○ Other _____
- ○ Other _____
- ○ Other _____
- ○ Other _____

"In the SIFT, you'll shine light on the lies you told yourself."

Step 3: SIFT

The SIFT is where you really start to gain your power. Please reference the SIFT worksheet to answer the following questions.

What is the narrative you told yourself? In what ways did you judge, criticize, or attack yourself?

_____

_____

In what ways did you judge, criticize, or attack the "other"?

_____

_____

Are there any thoughts that you can identify as being untrue?

_____

_____

What was revealed to you in the sift?

_____

_____

What assumptions have you made about yourself and others?

_____

_____

Finish this sentence. If only I was _____ , _____ , and

_____ .

What negative narratives do you most often experience? Please refer
to the sift worksheet.

_____

_____

My STIR beliefs were:	They brought up emotions of:	My reactions were:

STEP *4*

SHARE your vulnerable
stir story and what came up
in the SIT and the SIFT.

S
H
A
R
E

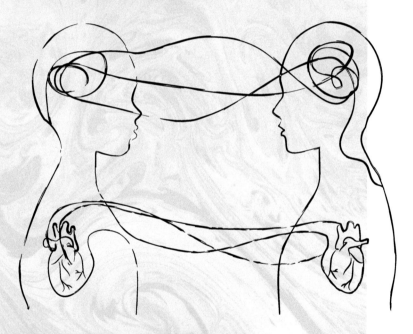

*"We liberate ourselves and others when we SHARE
our STIR stories.*

TINAMARIE CLARK

Step 4: SHARE

The SHARE is the cornerstone of the Shift Stirrer Method.

As a human being, without connection there would be no you. When we deny our need for others we suffer. Everyone seeks to be seen, heard, and felt. The share is a place to acknowledge our need for connection, share our stir stories, and gain powerful insights that may change our original perceptions.

Sharing the shameful, embarrassing, and raw parts of our stir stories allows us to liberate ourselves and others from the darkness and heaviness of the stir story. The by-products of the share are human connection and cultivation of intimacy —"Into me you see." You may be sharing about how you seem to always attract the same guy who you know isn't good for you while someone else is stirring about how their image never appears as flawless as their favorite on Instagram. No matter how different each person's stir story is, they carry a common thread of suffering. We are all #samesamebutdifferent.

Please go into the share free of expectations. A successful share is one in which you share your stir story openly and honestly with a responsive person. A supportive response is always hoped for but not required for a share to be successful. I recommend sharing your stir story with someone with whom you have a "soulship," or friendship of the soul, a person who hears and sees you.

Share your #stirstory as often as you can; we humans are all seeking meaningful, authentic connections. Truly being seen can be scary but the rewards outweigh the risks.

Name one or two people you trust and with whom you're willing to share your unfiltered stir story.

Name one: _____

Name two: _____

Describe your share in three words:

1. _____

2. _____

3. _____

Name three feelings and/or thoughts that came up for you during the share:

1. _____

2. _____

3. _____

SHIFT your perception through the wisdom that has been unearthed from working the steps.

"True self-mastery begins in the darkest corners in your internal walls. When you can SIT, SIFT, and SHARE you can SHIFT anything."

TINAMARIE CLARK

I honor you for making space to create a SHIFT
and for your willingness to make your subconscious
conscious.

Instead of playing the blame game, you are taking responsibility for your
#stirstory and choosing to write a new narrative.

The Shift Stirrer Method is meant to be integrated into your day-to-day life.
Every time you practice it, you nourish seeds, into new fertile ground. Be
patient and gentle with yourself during this process to reap all the beauty of
what will soon grow.

It's critical to know that your circumstances may not change but that the
narrative you attach to it may shift at any time. Your shifts may vary in
magnitude. Some may seem subtle while others seem massively life
changing. Please share the empowered narrative you are now choosing to go
forward with.

I'd like you to congratulate yourself and acknowledge your dedication to personal growth! I believe each of the five steps truly stand on their own. Consider yourself successful to even tackle one step. These steps are jam packed with opportunities to bring your subconscious conscious and shift your perception.

Which was the easiest step for you?

_____

_____

Which was the hardest step for you?

_____

_____

What is one piece of advice you'd give yourself after working the Shift Stirrer Method?

_____

_____

What has been one major lesson as a result of working the Shift Stirrer Method?

_____

_____

Using the prompt below, rewrite your story from start to finish and include any details you have unearthed using the Shift Stirrer Method. Add anything that feels relevant to you.

I was stirred most by _____ .

It felt _____ and _____ .

As I was in the sit, I realized _____ and

_____ .

I usually comfort myself by _____ and

_____ .

In the sift, I was surprised to see the thoughts of _____

and _____ .

In sharing my stir story, I felt _____ .

The main lesson for me here is _____ .

Name three feelings that describe your shift.

1. _____

2. _____

3. _____

Describe the shift in a color.

_____

It's time to affirm your shift in perception. Choose two words from the sift worksheet (pages 32-33) to create your personal shift mantra. Now use the following page to share your personal favorite shift mantra.

I'm <u>dismissed</u>. $\longrightarrow$ <u>I'm heard, seen and felt.</u>
I'm <u>scared</u>. $\longrightarrow$ <u>Today, I will feel the fear and do it anyway.</u>

I'm " _____ " $\longrightarrow$ " _____ "

I'm " _____ " $\longrightarrow$ " _____ "

I'm " _____ " $\longrightarrow$ " _____ "

I'm " _____ " $\longrightarrow$ " _____ "

Step 5: SHIFT

"

"

@SHIFTSTIRRERMETHOD / @TINAMARIECLARK

The Shift Stirrer Method

Congrats, Shifster! You are now part of the Shift Stirrer Community.

Share your story to empower yourself and your community through your brave and bold work. Tag us on social at @shiftstirrermethod and @tinamarieclark using #stirstory. Submit your stories online at www.shiftstirrer.com for a chance to be featured by TinaMarie.

———

NOW GO FORTH AND
#OWNYOURAWFUL

NOTES

Made in the USA
Monee, IL
20 November 2019